Edward Alan Freed

INDEX

A THIRD LADYBIRD BOOK OF

Nursery Rhymes

with illustrations
by FRANK HAMPSON

Ladybird Books Ltd Loughborough

Three blind mice, see how they run!

They all ran after the farmer's wife;

She cut off their tails
with a carving knife,

Did ever you see such
a thing in your life,

As three blind mice?

0 7214 0193 7

Curly-locks, Curly-locks,

Wilt thou be mine?

Thou shalt not wash dishes

Nor yet feed the swine,

But sit on a cushion

And sew a fine seam,

And feed upon strawberries,

Sugar and cream.

Tweedledum and Tweedledee
Agreed to have a battle,
For Tweedledum said Tweedledee
Had spoiled his nice new rattle.
Just then flew by a monstrous crow,
As big as a tar barrel,
Which frightened both the heroes so,
They quite forgot their quarrel.

I had a little pony,
His name was Dapple Grey:
I lent him to a lady
To ride a mile away.

She whipped him, she lashed him,
She rode him through the mire;
I would not lend my pony now,
For all the lady's hire.

The man in the moon

Came down too soon,

And asked his way to Norwich,

He went by the south,

And burnt his mouth

With eating cold plum porridge.

Tom, he was a piper's son,
He learned to play when he was young,
But all the tune that he could play
Was, "Over the hills and far away."
Over the hills and a great way off,
The wind will blow my top-knot off.

Tom with his pipe made such a noise,
That he pleased both the girls and boys,
And they all stopped to hear him play,
"Over the hills and far away."

Cross-patch,

Draw the latch,

Sit by the fire and spin;

Take a cup,

And drink it up,

Then call your neighbours in.

There was an old woman
tossed up in a basket,

Seventeen times as high
as the moon;

Where she was going
I couldn't but ask her,

For in her hand she carried a broom.

Old woman, old woman,
old woman, quoth I,

Where are you going to up so high?

To brush the cobwebs off the sky!

May I go with you?

Yes, by-and-by.

Higgledy Piggledy, my black hen,

She lays eggs for gentlemen;

Sometimes nine and sometimes ten,

Higgledy Piggledy, my black hen.

Oh! the grand old Duke of York,

He had ten thousand men;

He marched them up
to the top of the hill,

And he marched them down again.

And when they were up they were up,

And when they were down
they were down,

And when they were only half-way up,

They were neither up nor down.

I do not like thee, Doctor Fell,

The reason why I cannot tell;

But this I know, and know full well,

I do not like thee, Doctor Fell.

There was a crooked man,
  and he walked a crooked mile,
He found a crooked sixpence
  against a crooked stile;
He bought a crooked cat,
  which caught a crooked mouse,
And they all lived together
  in a little crooked house.

Come, let's to bed,

Says Sleepy-head ;

Tarry a while, says Slow ;

Put on the pan,

Says Greedy Nan,

Let's sup before we go.

Ding, dong, bell,
Pussy's in the well.
Who put her in?
Little Johnny Green.
Who pulled her out?
Little Tommy Stout.

What a naughty boy was that,
To try to drown poor pussy cat,
Who never did him any harm,
And killed the mice in his
father's barn.

The Queen of Hearts
She made some tarts,
All on a summer's day;
The Knave of Hearts
He stole the tarts,
And took them right away.

The King of Hearts,
Called for the tarts,
And beat the Knave full sore;
The Knave of Hearts
Brought back the tarts,
And vowed he'd steal no more.

Two legs sat upon three legs

With one leg in his lap;

In comes four legs

And runs away with one leg;

Up jumps two legs,

Catches up three legs,

Throws it after four legs,

And makes him bring back one leg.

Bobby Shafto's gone to sea,

Silver buckles on his knee;

He'll come back and marry me,

Bonny Bobby Shafto!

Bobby Shafto's fat and fair,

Combing down his yellow hair.

He's my love for ever more

Bonny Bobby Shafto!

For want of a nail
the shoe was lost,

For want of a shoe
the horse was lost,

For want of a horse
the rider was lost,

For want of a rider
the battle was lost,

For want of a battle
the kingdom was lost,

And all for the want
of a horseshoe nail.

US

Simple Simon met a pieman,
Going to the fair,
Says Simple Simon to the pieman,
Let me taste your ware.

Says the pieman to Simple Simon,
Show me first your penny;
Says Simple Simon to the pieman,
Indeed I have not any.

Simple Simon went a-fishing,
For to catch a whale;
All the water he had got
Was in his mother's pail.

Simple Simon went to look
If plums grew on a thistle,
He pricked his finger very much;
Which made poor Simon whistle.

ANTONIO

Fiddle-de-dee, fiddle-de-dee,

The fly shall marry the bumble-bee.

They went to the church,
and married was she:

The fly has married the bumble-bee.

FLY B

Rub-a-dub-dub,

Three men in a tub,

And how do you think
they got there?

The butcher, the baker,

The candlestick-maker,

They all jumped out of a
rotten potato,

'Twas enough to make a man stare.

Sing a song of sixpence,
A pocket full of rye;
Four and twenty blackbirds,
Baked in a pie.

When the pie was opened,
The birds began to sing;
Now wasn't that a dainty dish,
To set before the king?

The king was in his counting-house,
Counting out his money;
The queen was in the parlour,
Eating bread and honey.

The maid was in the garden,
Hanging out the clothes,
When down came a blackbird,
And pecked off her nose.

As I was going to St. Ives,

I met a man with seven wives,

Each wife had seven sacks,

Each sack had seven cats,

Each cat had seven kits:

Kits, cats, sacks and wives,

How many were going to St. Ives?

I saw a ship a-sailing,
    A-sailing on the sea,
And oh! but it was laden
    With pretty things for me.

There were comfits in the cabin,
    And apples in the hold;
The sails were made of silk,
    And the masts were made of gold.

The four and twenty sailors,
    Who stood upon the deck,
Were four and twenty white mice
    With chains about their necks.

The captain was a duck,
    With a packet on his back,
And when the ship began to move,
    The captain cried Quack! Quack!

Series 413